WII Shapes

Written by Annemarie Young
and illustrated by Nick Schon,
based on the original characters
created by Roderick Hunt and Alex Brychta

OXFORD
UNIVERSITY PRESS

It was Wilf's birthday and all
his friends were there. They were
going on a treasure hunt for
shapes.

"You've each got a different
shape," said Dad.

"See how many things you can
find in that shape," said Mum.

Anna's circles

Find these circles in the picture.
Can you find any others?

Anna found lots of circles. She
even found one she could eat –
a chocolate biscuit.

Sam's squares

Find these squares in the picture.
Can you find any others?

Sam found lots of squares. He
even found one he could eat –
a waffle.

Wilma's rectangles

Find these rectangles in the picture.
Can you find any others?

Wilma found lots of rectangles.
She found one she could eat –
a flapjack.

Chip's triangles

Find these triangles in the picture.
Can you find any others?

Chip found lots of triangles.
He found one he could eat –
a slice of pizza.

Find these spheres in the picture.
Can you find any others?

14

Biff found lots of spheres. She
found one she could eat –
an orange.

Kipper's cones

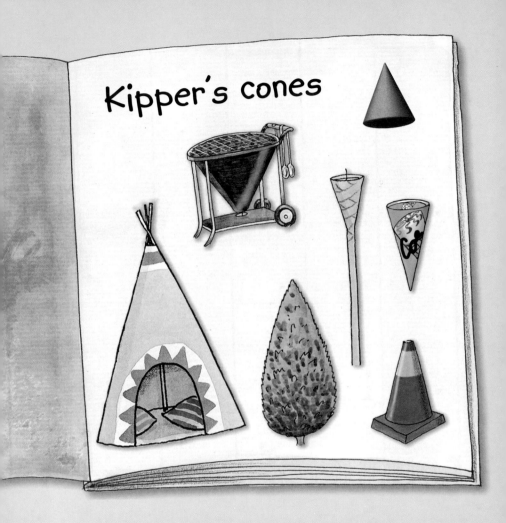

Find these cones in the picture.
Can you find any others?

Kipper found lots of cones,
and an ice cream cone, too.

Nadim's pyramids

Find these pyramids in the picture.
Can you find any others?

Nadim found lots of pyramids. He
even found one he could eat – a fruit
jelly made in the shape of a pyramid!

Anneena's cubes

Find these cubes in the picture.
Can you find any others?

Anneena found lots of cubes.
She found one she could eat –
a small iced cake.

Hong's cylinders

Find these cylinders in the picture.
Can you find any others?

Hong found lots of cylinders.
He even found one he could eat –
a mini chocolate roll.

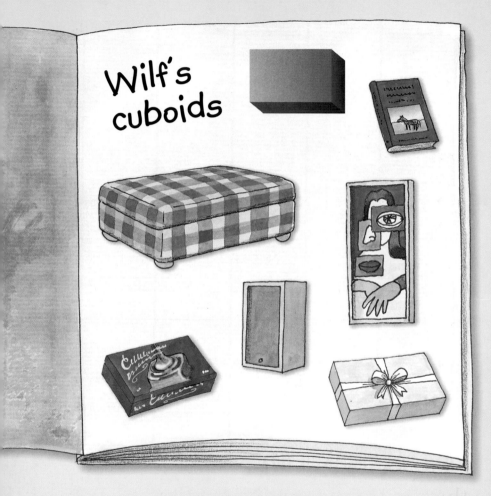

Wilf's cuboids

Find these cuboids in the picture.
Can you find any others?

Wilf found lots of cuboids. One of them was a box of chocolates.

"What's in that big box?" he asked.

"Surprise!" said Mum and Dad.

Talk about shapes

Can you find some circles on every page of the story?

Which shapes is the clown juggling?

Which shaped treats would you most like to eat?

What shapes can you find in your house?

Building with shapes

Which shapes did Wilf use?

I used a triangle for the roof.

Why don't you make something out of shapes?

Spot the difference

Find the five differences in the two pictures.